What Else Can I
Alto Saxopho
Grade Three

St. Patrick's Day

Words by Thomas Moore, Music from Playford's 'Dancing Master'

This tune appeared in a collection called 'The English Dancing Master' published by John Playford in 1650. Playford, a friend of Samuel Pepys, wrote 'Introduction To The Skill Of Musick' (1654) which was the standard textbook on the subject for nearly a century.

The rhythm should have a light skip to it, your tongue needs to work quite fast where the notes are dotted. It is a busy tune, make sure you take enough breath to sustain each phrase. There's a pause in bar 14 where you might recover if you're in trouble!

The happy wanderer
(Val-de-ri val-de-ra)

Words by Antonia Ridge, Music by F W Moller

Whenever a group of hikers is getting weary, perhaps hungry and cold or maybe lost, the chances are that some bright spark will pipe up with this song!

Play with a full tone, lightly tonguing the repeated notes. Try to produce the same quality of sound on Cs and Bs, they can sound a little 'thin'. In the crescendo from bar 20 through to bar 26, you can use your attack of the long tied notes as steps up, then peak with the first note of bar 27. Use the tip of your tongue on the reed for the staccato run down.

Autumn leaves
(Les feuilles mortes)

English Words by Johnny Mercer, French Words by Jacques Prévert, Music by Joseph Kosma

Jacques Prévert (1900–1977), who wrote the words of 'Les Feuilles Mortes', was one of France's most celebrated film-makers. He didn't start writing poetry until he was 46, but was soon placed as one of the greatest modern French poets too. Several of his poems have been set to music.

'Autumn Leaves' is a slow and beautiful piece, needing a rich warm tone. Play as smoothly as possible, the phrases should sound free and flowing without any individual notes sticking out. For playing across wide pitch intervals you may need to adjust your embouchure slightly, to make low and high notes sound even. Try counting in four the first time through, looking carefully at the ties.

La vie en rose

Original French Words by Edith Piaf, English Words by Mack David, Music by Louiguy

This song was made famous by French singer, Edith Piaf (1915–1963) who also wrote the words. Her singing career began on the streets of Paris, where she earned the nickname 'piaf' or little sparrow. Actress and singer Grace Jones also had a top twenty hit with this song in 1986.

You will need plenty of breath for this piece. The phrases require good control, don't rush or allow notes to leap out suddenly. Be especially careful with your intonation through the crescendo which starts at bar 13, don't let the notes go flat as you increase volume!

Forty-Second Street

Words by Al Dubin, Music by Harry Warren

This was the title song of the theatre musical and the film of 1932, and was sung by Dick Powell and Ruby Keeler as they danced on top of a taxi cab. The story was also used for another filmed musical from the same period, *The Gold Diggers of 1933*, for which songwriters Al Dubin and Harry Warren also wrote the music.

Let the tune swing along in a relaxed, unhurried style. Careful attention to the articulation should help you produce a really colourful performance. Be ready with your fourth finger (left hand) for the G sharp.

My funny valentine

Words by Lorenz Hart, Music by Richard Rodgers

Between the years 1918 and 1942 the writing partnership of Richard Rodgers and Lorenz Hart produced a string of wonderful songs including such classics as 'Manhattan', 'Thou Swell', 'The Lady is a Tramp' and 'I Could Write a Book'. When Hart retired, Rodgers went on to further extraordinary success in his partnership with Oscar Hammerstein II.

This tune is quiet and soulful. Try to breathe gently into the phrases, taking care not to tongue too harshly. Gradually build up in volume and intensity, working toward the peak at bar 35. Maintain the forte on the top C, then make a complete break, for maximum effect, before resuming the tune for the last few bars.

Cabaret

Words by Fred Ebb, Music by John Kander

This is the title song from the musical set in a sleazy Berlin nightclub in the 1930s. The show opened in New York in 1966 and ran for well over one thousand performances. In 1972 it was made into a film, starring Liza Minnelli and Joel Grey.

The tune has a syncopated rhythm, aim for the first beat in each bar to keep yourself on track. There are a few accidentals to contend with; the E flat is the same fingering as D sharp and the A sharp is best played with the long fingering.

Rhythm of the rain

Words and Music by John C Gummoe

John Gummoe was the singer and guitarist with The Cascades, who had a hit with this song in 1963. The Cascades are not remembered for much else, but the song has become a pop classic which still receives a fair amount of radio play. Jason Donavon also had a top ten hit with this song in 1990.

Notice the key signature! There aren't many E flats to play, but be ready with that fourth finger (right hand) in bar 21, and make sure it is firmly under control. Play legato, keeping the notes evenly spaced.

Summer holiday

Words and Music by Bruce Welch and Brian Bennett

The film *Summer Holiday* (1963) starred Cliff Richard and Lauri Peters. It is a light-hearted trip across Europe in a double-decker bus, with various adventures along the way. Bruce Welch and Brian Bennett, who wrote this song, were both members of The Shadows, Cliff's backing group, and they also appear in the film.

This should be played with a swing, so relax the dotted quavers, the rhythm doesn't want to sound too rigid. In bar 15 the hands need to be kept closely in position when changing between D and C.

The hundred pipers

Words by Lady Nairne, Music traditional

This is a Scottish ballad which celebrates the Jacobite rebellion of 1745. Bonnie Prince Charlie, grandson of James II, won the support of the Scottish Highlanders and invaded England, marching as far south as Derby. The song is attributed to Carolina, Baroness Nairne (1766–1845) who also wrote 'Charlie Is My Darling'.

Be careful with the semiquaver rhythm which begins several phrases. Space the notes evenly and lean onto the first beat of the bar, imagining the drone of bagpipes! Listen carefully to your intonation, especially when the melody reaches the high notes at bars 12 and 16.

© 1996 International Music Publications Limited, Woodford Green, Essex IG8 8HN

We need a little Christmas

Words and Music by Jerry Herman

This song is from the American musical comedy *Mame* which opened on Broadway in 1966, starring Angela Lansbury in the title-role. Writer Jerry Herman also created the outstandingly successful *Hello, Dolly!* (1964).

You might like to warm up with your B flat major scale before playing this piece! There are several E flats to watch out for and the complete B flat scale makes up the end of the song. Keep the phrases moving using a light tone and be sure to use the rests for their rhythmic 'kick'.

The shadow of your smile

Words by Paul Francis Webster, Music by Johnny Mandel

This song is from the film *The Sandpiper* (1965) which starred Richard Burton and Elizabeth Taylor. It won both the Academy Award for Best Song and a Grammy Award in the same year.

There are long legato phrases in this piece but you also have intervals to leap, from high to low notes and *vice versa*. Make sure the register key is released each time, so that notes sound in the correct octave (careful positioning of the thumb is necessary). Beware of accidentals!

Moonlight serenade

Words by Mitchell Parish, Music by Glenn Miller

Moonlight Serenade was a hit for American bandleader Glenn Miller in 1939. It is said that he wrote the piece purely as an exercise but it became known as his signature tune. In 1942 Miller joined the military, to become director of the American Air Force Band. Two years later, a light plane in which he was travelling to Paris, disappeared without trace over the English Channel.

Carefully controlled playing is required here, the quaver triplets must be kept even and not rushed. In the middle section there are triplets over two beats, try giving these a really 'drawn out' feel. Your tone should remain steady throughout, this is made difficult by some awkward intervals and a crescendo in the upper register.

Blueberry Hill

Words and Music by Al Lewis, Larry Stock and Vincent Rose

Rhythm and blues giant Fats Domino, from New Orleans, was in the UK charts with this song in 1956 and again in 1976. When he first started recording, Fats Domino's relaxed and laid back musical style was considered by producers to be slightly too slow for the market, so they sped up the tapes!

Aim for a warm, lazy sound and spread the notes out evenly. There are some interval leaps for which you'll need your thumb ready with the register key. The melody features a rising arpeggio, in C major, so here's a chance to put all that serious practise to good use!

From Russia with love

Words and Music by Lionel Bart

This is the theme song from the James Bond film of the same name and it was a hit for singer Matt Monro in 1963. The composer Lionel Bart also enjoyed great success with his songs 'Rock With The Caveman', 'Little White Bull', 'Living Doll' and, perhaps best known, his musical show *Oliver!*.

The minor key helps create a sense of drama. Use plenty of tone and try to suggest a touch of sadness mingled with strong passion! You might find that the triplet rhythms, in bars 24 and 32, will also add to the intensity of emotion if you linger over them a little.

Valse lente
(from 'Coppélia')

Leo Delibes

This is the slow waltz from Delibes' ballet *Coppélia* (1870). Doctor Coppélius has created a beautiful clockwork doll, which entrances a young man of the village. The young man's girlfriend eventually plays a trick on him, changing places with the doll.

Sensitive playing will bring the best out of this pretty tune. Think ahead for where you are going to breathe, don't break the middle of phrases with gasps for air! The semiquavers should be smooth and swift, it might help to practise these separately first. Have your right hand ready for the bottom C, and remember to relax your embouchure a little to get a full round low note.

What Else Can I Play?
Alto Saxophone
Grade Three

	Piano part	Saxophone part
Autumn Leaves (Les Feuilles Mortes)	6	3
Blueberry Hill	26	14
Cabaret	12	7
Forty-Second Street	8	5
From Russia With Love	28	15
The Happy Wanderer (Val-de-ri Val-de-ra)	4	2
The Hundred Pipers	18	10
La Vie En Rose	7	4
Moonlight Serenade	24	13
My Funny Valentine	10	6
Rhythm Of The Rain	14	8
The Shadow Of Your Smile	22	12
St. Patrick's Day	3	1
Summer Holiday	16	9
Valse Lente (From 'Coppelia')	30	16
We Need A Little Christmas	20	11

Series Editor: Mark Mumford

Music arranged and processed by
Barnes Music Engraving Ltd
East Sussex TN22 4HA, England

Published 1996

Introduction

In this *What Else Can I Play?* collection you'll find sixteen popular tunes that are both challenging and entertaining.

The pieces have been carefully selected and arranged to create ideal supplementary material for young saxophonists who are either working towards or have recently taken a Grade Three saxophone examination.

As the student progresses through the volume, technical demands increase and new concepts are introduced which reflect the requirements of the major Examination Boards. Suggestions and guidelines on breathing, dynamics and tempo are given for each piece, together with technical tips and performance notes.

Pupils will experience a wide variety of music, ranging from folk and classical through to showtunes and popular songs, leading to a greater awareness of musical styles.

Whether it's for light relief from examination preparation, or to reinforce the understanding of new concepts, this collection will enthuse and encourage all young saxophone players.

Note: references to fingering within this book use Thumb 1 2 3 4.

St. Patrick's Day

Words by Thomas Moore, Music from Playford's 'Dancing Master'

The happy wanderer
(Val-de-ri val-de-ra)

Words by Antonia Ridge, Music by F W Moller

Autumn leaves
(Les feuilles mortes)

English Words by Johnny Mercer, French Words by Jacques Prévert, Music by Joseph Kosma

La vie en rose

Original French Words by Edith Piaf, English Words by Mack David, Music by Louiguy

Forty-Second Street

Words by Al Dubin, Music by Harry Warren

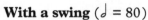

B Feldman & Co Ltd, London WC2H 0EA

My funny valentine

Words by Lorenz Hart, Music by Richard Rodgers

Cabaret

Words by Fred Ebb, Music by John Kander

Rhythm of the rain

Words and Music by John C Gummoe

Summer holiday

Words and Music by Bruce Welch and Brian Bennett

The hundred pipers

Words by Lady Nairne, Music traditional

We need a little Christmas

Words and Music by Jerry Herman

The shadow of your smile

Words by Paul Francis Webster, Music by Johnny Mandel

Moonlight serenade

Words by Mitchell Parish, Music by Glenn Miller

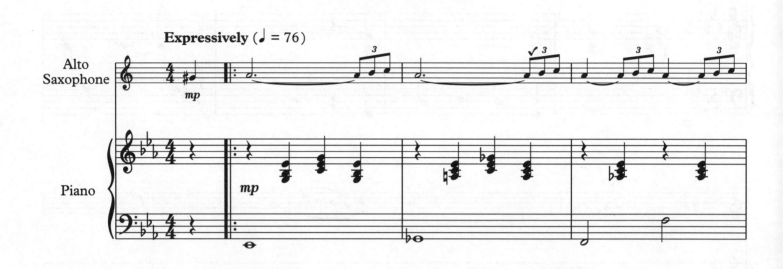

Blueberry Hill

Words and Music by Al Lewis, Larry Stock and Vincent Rose

From Russia with love

Words and Music by Lionel Bart

Valse lente
(from 'Coppélia')

Leo Delibes